When I sit on the bank,
where the river flows,
the smell is so bad
that I hold my nose.

When I stand near the factory
and the wind's from the south,
it stings my eyes
and blows grit in my mouth.

With all these horrible
things in the air,
I need a gas mask
to go anywhere.

Charles Thomson

Green Poems

Compiled by John Foster

Contents

Acknowledgements

The Editor and Publisher wish to thank the following who have kindly given permission for the use of copyright material:

John Foster for 'Stop!', 'We've got to start recycling' and 'We must protect the countryside' all © 1993 John Foster; Brian Moses for 'The bird on the shore' © 1993 Brian Moses; Charles Thomson for 'I need a gas mask' © 1993 Charles Thomson; Irene Yates for 'Grandad says' © 1993 Irene Yates.

I need a gas mask

When I walk around town,
it's really busy
and the smell of car fumes
makes me dizzy.

When I go in the café
for a drink and a cake,
the cigarette smoke
makes my head ache.

The bird on the shore

A sticky skin of oil
is floating on the sea
and any bird caught in it
needs our help to break free.

Just like the gull we found,
half-dead among the sands.
We wrapped him in a towel
but still he pecked Dad's hands.

'It's not a job for us,' Dad said,
'He needs some expert care.
I think I know a place.
They'll make him better there.'

They scrubbed and cleaned our gull,
then showed us several more,
which had been black with oil
and half-dead on the shore.

A sticky skin of oil
is floating on the sea
and any bird caught in it
needs our help to break free.

Brian Moses

We've got to start recycling

Take all your old glass bottles
To the bottle bank in town,
So they can use the glass again
By melting it all down.

Don't dump your old newspapers
With the rubbish in the tip.
Save them all, then put them
In the green recycling skip.

Don't throw away your drink cans,
Their metal's useful too.
We've got to start recycling.
It's up to me and you!

John Foster

Grandad says

On the pavements, in the streets,
Bags from crisps, wrappers from sweets.
Rubbish rots in roads and gutters.
'What a mess!' Grandad mutters.
'Keep things tidy, keep things clean.
Make the world fit to be seen.'

Irene Yates

We must protect the countryside

We must protect the countryside—
the flowers and the trees.
We must protect the animals.
It's up to you and me.

Don't throw litter on the ground.
Please put it in a bin,
And close the gate behind you
To keep the cattle in.

Keep your dog upon a lead.
Don't let it run away.
Stay on the paths. Don't wander
Through the fields of wheat or hay.

Don't leave a broken bottle
Lying on the grass,
Or it could start a fire
Like a magnifying glass.

Don't poke around in birds' nests
Or chase creatures that you see.
Don't pull up plants or flowers
Or break branches off a tree.

Don't squeeze through gaps in hedges.
Please use the stiles or gates.
Don't pollute the water

With rubbish or lead weights.

We must protect the animals,
the trees, the plants, the flowers.
We must protect the countryside.
Remember that it's ours.

John Foster

Stop

Stop chopping down the trees,
please.

The animals need the trees.
The forest is their home.

Stop chopping down the trees,
PLEASE.

John Foster